The Penguin Music Scores

EDITED BY GORDON JACOB

BRAHMS

Violin Concerto in D, Op. 77

WITH AN INTRODUCTION BY
GORDON JACOB

PENGUIN BOOKS

PENGUIN BOOKS

Published by the Penguin Group
27 Wrights Lane, London W8 5TZ, England
Viking Penguin Inc., 40 West 23rd Street, New York, New York 10010, USA
Penguin Books Australia Ltd, Ringwood, Victoria, Australia
Penguin Books Canada Ltd, 2801 John Street, Markham, Ontario, Canada L3R 1B4
Penguin Books (NZ) Ltd, 182–190 Wairau Road, Auckland 10, New Zealand

Penguin Books Ltd, Registered Offices: Harmondsworth, Middlesex, England

Published in Penguin Books 1954
3 5 7 9 10 8 6 4 2

Introduction copyright © 1954 by Gordon Jacob
All rights reserved

Made and printed in Great Britain by
Richard Clays Ltd (The Chaucer Press), Bungay, Suffolk

JOHANNES BRAHMS (1833–97)
VIOLIN CONCERTO IN D, Op. 77

THIS concerto was first performed on New Year's day 1879 by Joseph Joachim, for whom it was written. It had been on the stocks for a considerable time and its publication had been delayed by the fact that the solo part took a long time to reach its final shape. Brahms was not a violinist and he therefore had to rely a great deal on the advice and suggestions of Joachim in order to ensure that the violin part should be laid out as effectively as possible. Brahms disliked virtuosity for its own sake and was anxious that the musical value of the concerto should not be impaired by mere fireworks. Joachim was himself a composer of distinction and serious aims who was a close friend of Brahms and a great admirer of his music. The partnership was therefore an ideal one, and a fine balance was eventually attained whereby the symphonic stature of the work took precedence over technical display, without the solo part suffering in any way from lack of brilliance and violinistic effectiveness. Joachim himself wrote the cadenza for the first performance. His cadenza is still the one most frequently played, and rightly so, for, apart from its excellence, it must have had the full approval of the composer. In this connexion one may recall the collaboration of David, W. H. Reed, and Heifetz with Mendelssohn, Elgar, and Walton respectively in fixing the final form of the solo parts in their violin concertos.

The work is conceived on a very large scale and is comparable in length and importance with Beethoven's violin concerto. The size of the orchestra is, however, modest. It is the normal classical orchestra without trombones but with a second pair of horns. Although valve-horns and trumpets had been in use for many years when this score was written, Brahms had very decided ideas about the superiority of the open notes of the harmonic series and, to the end of his life, used as few notes as possible outside the limited range of the 'natural' instruments. This accounts for his use of one pair of horns in D and one in E in the first and last movements.

The first movement returns to classical precedent in opening with an extended *tutti* before the entry of the solo violin. In this *tutti* most of the thematic material of the movement is stated. When the solo instrument does come in it is some time (bar 136) before he settles down to his exposition of the themes. A bridge-passage (bar 164), in which the violin has, first, chordal passages and then semiquaver figuration above the leaping octave figure (first heard at bar 17 in the *tutti*), leads into the second subject at bar 178. A charming pendant to the second subject, not previously heard in the *tutti*, begins at bar 206 and is followed by the vigorous passage (bar 246) which the orchestra has already announced towards the end of the *tutti* (bar 78). It will be noted that the themes all occur in the tonic key in the *tutti* whereas the normal dominant key is employed for the second subject material in the second exposition by the solo instrument. This is in accordance with the procedure of Mozart in his concertos.

The development begins at bar 272 with another extended *tutti* in which all the themes are touched upon. A new rhythmical figure appears on the solo violin at bar 312. This dominates the scene until bar

348, where some discussion of the leaping octave figure takes place. At bar 361 begins a passage which works up to the recapitulation (bar 381) which is started by the full orchestra emphatically stating the first subject. The themes return in the same order as before with some modifications, a brief *tutti* at bar 513 ushering in the cadenza with the conventional 6-4 chord at bar 525. The coda starts quietly at bar 527 but works up to a brilliant ending. At the *animato* (bar 559) the brass and drums have the rhythm of the vigorous bridge-passage, first heard at bar 78.

The second movement is in the rather unexpected key of F, but the listener is led into the key gently by the bassoons which suggest D minor until the horns dispel this illusion with their C in the second bar. The oboe then plays a very beautiful melody accompanied entirely by the wind instruments. Only one pair of horns is used in this movement and the trumpets and drums are silent. The scoring of this opening wind-passage requires much careful attention to balance. The most ardent champion of Brahms cannot claim that it is well conceived orchestrally. The effect is thick and turgid, especially where the bassoons play in octaves with the second horn growling in between. But the melody is ideally suited to the oboe, both in spirit and actual range of notes, and this compensates in great measure for the turgid harmonization. Fortunately Brahms uses the strings to accompany the solo violin when it comes in, and the little comments by the wind instruments are delightful. The form is simple – ternary or aria form. The presentation of the original melody at bar 78 is beautifully done. The layout of the wind instruments from bar 83 is much more agreeable in sound than it is at the beginning of the movement, and the strings give relief at bar 87 and also (*pizzicato*) from bar 91 to the wind tone. The beauty of the music all through this passage is not marred by any indiscretions of scoring. We expect a certain amount of thickness of texture from Brahms; it is part of his style and suits the seriousness of his temperament. It is only occasionally that it becomes a little oppressive.

Joachim was a Hungarian and it was largely through his influence that Brahms became interested in Hungarian and gipsy music. It was appropriate therefore that the finale of this concerto should reflect this interest. The movement is gay and unrestrained and comes as a tremendous and welcome contrast to the gravity of the preceding movements. It is in free rondo form. We use the word 'free' because there is a good deal of development of the themes and it is not in any way formal in its effect. The main themes are (a) the one heard at the beginning with its responsive section at bar 17 and return at bar 27; (b) the upward rising theme in octaves on the solo violin at bar 57; and (c) the theme in triple time at bar 128.

Brahms is careful to avoid too much squareness of rhythm in his principal subject, as is shown in bars 31–3. The writing for the solo violin shows great brilliance throughout the movement, and much of the figuration could only have been devised by a violinist. Joachim seems to have been given an especially free hand here in his editing of the solo part, not only in the way of rearranging passages so as to lie well for the left hand, but also in the all-important matter of bowing, the details of which can often only be settled by actual trial on the instrument.

The coda begins at bar 222 and falls into two parts, the second starting at the *Poco fini presto* which follows the short cadenza at bar 266. In the second part of the coda the principal theme is presented in 6-8 time (written as triplets) and there is also some fresh treatment of theme (b) and its inversion (beginning at bar 292). The ending is as original as it is effective. Instead of finishing with a flourish Brahms lets the music die away into the distance, the final *forte*, not *fortissimo*, chords being added by way of a full stop.

The concerto is one of Brahms' finest works. The themes and their working out are marked throughout by the greatest felicities of invention. It has retained for seventy-five years a proud and honoured place in the limited repertoire of first-rate violin concertos and will continue to do so for a long time to come. It is a splendid example of virtuosity being made to serve purely musical ends.

A word or two may be added about the transposing instruments. Clarinets in A are used in the first and last movements. These sound a minor third lower than written. In the slow movement clarinets in B flat are employed. These sound a tone lower than written. Horns in D transpose a minor seventh and in E a minor sixth down except when their parts are written in the bass clef. They then transpose *up* a whole tone and a major third respectively. In the slow movement horns in F are used. These transpose down a fifth when written in the treble clef and a fourth *up* in the bass clef. Trumpets in D transpose up a whole tone.

JOHANNES BRAHMS (1833–97)
VIOLINKONZERT IN D, Op. 77

DIESES Konzert wurde am 1. Januar 1879 zum erstenmal aufgeführt. Joseph Joachim, für den Brahms es schrieb, war der Solist. Die Herausgabe war dadurch verzögert worden, dass die Solopartie erst nach langer Zeit ihre endgültige Form erreichte. Brahms war kein Geiger und hatte sich deshalb auf Joachims Rat und Anregungen zu verlassen, um der Geige zur grösstmöglichen Wirksamkeit zu verhelfen. Brahms duldete keinerlei Effekthascherei, und war darauf bedacht, den musikalischen Gehalt des Konzerts nicht durch blosses Feuerwerk zu beeinträchtigen. Auch Joachim war ein vorzüglicher Komponist, ein intimer Freund von Brahms und grosser Bewunderer seiner Kunst. Die Zusammenarbeit der beiden Meister war deshalb ideal. Sie ergab ein vollkommenes Gleichgewicht zwischen der sinfonischen Gestaltung des Werkes und der Behandlung der Solostimme. Diese hatte den Vorrang vor Virtuosität um ihrer selbst willen, während es jener doch niemals an Glanz und geigerischer Wirksamkeit mangelte. Joachim selbst schrieb die Kadenz für die Erstaufführung. Sie wird auch heute noch meistens gespielt, und mit Recht, denn ganz abgesehen von ihrer Schönheit hatte sie natürlich Brahms' volle Billigung. In diesem Zusammenhang darf man auf die Zusammenarbeit zwischen Ferdinand David und Mendelssohn, W. H. Reed und Elgar, Heifetz und William Walton hinweisen, in der Interpret und Komponist die endgültige Form der Violinpartien gemeinsam festlegten.

Das Werk ist im grossen Masstab angelegt und in Länge und Bedeutung mit Beethovens Violinkonzert vergleichbar. Das Orchester ist jedoch im Umfang bescheiden, nämlich das normale klassische Orchester, ohne Posaunen aber mit einem zweiten Paar von Hörnern. Obschon Ventil-Hörner und -Trompeten seit Jahren in Gebrauch gewesen waren als diese Partitur geschrieben wurde, zog Brahms die in der natürlichen Obertonreihe vorkommenden Noten bei weitem vor: bis zum Ende seines Lebens verwendete er so wenig Noten ausserhalb der von den alten Blasinstrumenten gespielten Naturtöne wie möglich. Dies ist der Grund für seine Anwendung von zwei Hörnern in D und zweien in E im ersten und letzten Satz.

Dem Beispiel des klassischen Konzerts folgend, fängt der erste Satz mit einem ausgedehnten *Tutti* an, bevor die Solovioline ins Erscheinen tritt. In diesem *Tutti* wird fast das ganze thematische Material des Satzes dargestellt. Wenn dann die Geige hinzutritt, so dauert es einige Zeit bis sie zu ihrer Exposition der Themen kommt (136. Takt). Eine Überleitung (164. Takt), in der die Violine zunächst Akkorde spielt und dann Sechzehntel-Verzierungen über der im 17. Takt erstmalig gehörten springenden Oktaven-Figur, führt im 178. Takt zum zweiten Hauptthema. Ein reizendes Anhängsel, das noch nicht vorher im *Tutti* gehört wurde, fängt im 206. Takt an. Ihm folgt (246. Takt) eine kraftvolle Stelle, die das Orchester bereits kurz vor dem Ende des *Tutti*, im 78. Takt, angekündigt hatte. Während aber alle Themen im *Tutti* in der Grundtonart gespielt werden, wird das Material des zweiten Hauptthemas nun vom Soloinstrument in der Tonart der Oberdominante gebracht. Dies war auch Mozarts Praxis in seinen Konzerten.

Die Durchführung fängt mit dem 272. Takt an. Auch hier gibt es ein langes *Tutti*, in dem alle Themen berührt werden. Im 312. Takt spielt die Solovioline eine neue rhythmische Figur, die das Bild bis zum 348. Takt beherrscht, wo dann eine weitere Diskussion der springenden Oktaven-Figur stattfindet. Im 361. Takt beginnt eine Passage, die beim 381. Takt zur Wiederholung führt. Diese beginnt mit dem ersten Thema, vom ganzen Orchester mit vollem Nachdruck gespielt. Die Themen kehren in der gleichen Reihenfolge wieder wie zuvor, jedoch mit einigen Abänderungen. Ein kurzes *Tutti* (513. Takt) kündet mit dem üblichen Quartsextakkord (525. Takt) die Kadenz an. Die Coda beginnt ruhig im 527. Takt, steigert sich aber zu einem glänzenden Abschluss. Im *Animato* (559. Takt) spielen die Blechbläser und Pauken den Rhythmus der kräftigen Überleitung, den wir zuerst im 78. Takt hörten.

Der zweite Satz ist in der recht unerwarteten Tonart F-dur, aber der Zuhörer wird sanft zu ihr geführt, denn die Fagotte deuten auf D-moll hin, bis die Hörner diese Illusion mit ihrem C im 2. Takt zerstören. Dann spielt die Oboe eine wunderbare Melodie, nur von Holzbläsern begleitet. In diesem Satz finden nur ein Paar Hörner Anwendung und die Trompeten und Pauken schweigen. Die Instrumentierung dieses Anfangs für Holzbläser erfordert ein äusserst sorgfältiges Abwägen der Klangstärke. Selbst der begeistertste Verfechter von Brahms kann nicht behaupten, dass die Stelle wirklich gut orchestriert ist. Sie macht einen schweren und schwülstigen Eindruck, besonders dann, wenn die Fagotte in Oktaven spielen und das zweite Horn dazwischenfährt. Die Melodie ist jedoch sowohl im Geiste wie im Aufbau für die Oboe ideal geeignet und entschädigt uns fast ganz für die schwerfällige Instrumentierung. Glücklicherweise wird die Solovioline bei ihrem Eintritt von Streichern begleitet, und die kleinen Bemerkungen der Bläser sind entzückend. Die Form des Satzes ist einfach: es ist die grosse dreiteilige Liedform. Von besonderer Schönheit ist das Erscheinen der ursprünglichen Melodie im 78. Takt. Auch die Anordnung der Blasinstrumente vom 83. Takt an ist klanglich viel besser als am Anfang des Satzes, besonders da die Streicher im 87.

Takt und vom 91. Takt an den Bläserton auflockern, im letzteren Falle durch *Pizzicato*. Diesmal wird die Schönheit der Musik durch keinerlei Mängel in der Orchestrierung gestört. Eine gewisse Undurchsichtigkeit in der Struktur erwarten wir von Brahms ohnehin: sie gehört zu seinem Stil und passt zu seiner ernsten Gesinnungsart. Nur gelegentlich werden wir davon ein wenig bedrückt.

Joachim war ein Ungar, und unter seinem Einfluss interessierte sich Brahms für ungarische und Zigeunermusik. Es ist deshalb durchaus verständlich, dass das Finale unseres Konzerts dieses Interesse widerspiegelt. Der Satz ist froh und unbeschwert und steht in starkem und willkommenem Gegensatz zum ernsten Geist der ersten beiden Sätze. Die Form ist die eines frei gestalteten Rondos. Wir sagen bewusst 'frei gestaltet', denn der Satz mangelt nicht an Durchführung der Themen und wirkt in keiner Weise formell. Die Hauptthemen sind (a) das am Anfang zu hörende Thema mit seiner Antwort (17. Takt) und der Wiederholung (27. Takt); (b) das von der Solovioline gespielte aufsteigende Thema in Oktaven (57. Takt); und (c) das Triolen-Thema vom 128. Takt an.

Mit Sorgfalt vermeidet Brahms eine zu grosse Kantigkeit im Rhythmus des Hauptthemas. Man sehe z.B. Takt 31 bis 33. Die Schreibart für die Solovioline ist während des ganzen Satzes voller Glanz. Viele der Figuren konnten nur von einem Geiger erdacht werden, und es scheint als hätte Joachim hier besonders freie Hand im Redigieren der Solostimme — nicht nur in der Anordnung von Passagen, sodass sie gut für die linke Hand liegen, sondern auch in der so wichtigen Frage der Bogenführung, deren Einzelheiten oft nur durch wirkliches Ausprobieren auf dem Instrument festgelegt werden können.

Die Coda beginnt mit dem 222. Takt und besteht aus zwei Teilen. Im zweiten Teil, der mit dem *Poco fini presto* am Ende der kurzen Kadenz (266. Takt) beginnt, wird das Hauptthema im 6/8-Takt gespielt (es ist in Triolen geschrieben). Auch das Thema (b) und seine Umkehrung werden (im 292. Takt beginnend) in neuer Weise behandelt. Der Schluss ist ebenso originell wie er wirkungsvoll ist. Statt mit fliegenden Fahnen zu enden, lässt Brahms die Musik hinwegebben. Nur die abschliessenden Akkorde, die *forte*, nicht *fortissimo*, markiert sind, werden gewissermassen als Schlusspunkt hinzugefügt.

Das Konzert ist eines der schönsten Werke von Brahms. Von Anfang bis Ende sind die Themen und ihre Verarbeitung voll der glücklichsten Einfälle. Seit 75 Jahren hat es einen Ehrenplatz in der erlesen Gesellschaft wirklich hervorragender Violinkonzerto eingenommen, und dieser Platz ist ihm auf lange Zeit hinaus sicher. Das Konzert ist ein ausgezeichnetes Beispiel dafür dass blosse Virtuosität sehr wohl in den Dienst der reinen Musik gestellt werden kann.

Noch ein paar Worte über die transponierenden Instrumente. A-Klarinetten kommen im ersten und letzten Satz zur Verwendung. Diese klingen eine kleine Terz tiefer als geschrieben. Im langsamen Satz werden B-Klarinetten benützt, welche einen Ton tiefer klingen als im Druck. Hörner in D transponieren eine verminderte Septe nach unten, und die in E eine verminderte Sexte, ausser wenn ihnen ein Bass-Schlüssel zuvorsteht: dann transponieren sie einen Ton, bzw. eine Terz nach *oben*. Im zweiten Satz kommen F-Hörner zur Anwendung. Diese transponieren eine Quinte nach unten, wenn im Violinschlüssel und eine Quarte *herauf*, wenn im Bass-Schlüssel. Trompeten in D transponieren einen ganzen Ton herauf.

JOHANNES BRAHMS (1833–97)

CONCIERTO DE VIOLIN EN RE, Op. 77

ESTE concierto fué ejecutado por orimera vez el día de Año Nuevo de 1879 por Joseph Joachim, para quien fué escrito. Se conservó inédito durante un tiempo considerable y su publicación fué retrasada por el hecho de que la parte de violín necesitó largas elaboraciones para llegar a su forma definitiva. Brahms no era violinista y por consiguiente tenía que confiar en gran parte en los consejos y sugerencias de Joachim a fin de asegurarse de que la ejecución fuese totalmente posible. Brahms no gustaba de la virtuosidad por sí misma y deseaba que el valor musical del concierto no se viera disminuido por meros fuegos de artificio. Joachim, que era también un compositor de cierta distinción y serios propósitos, era amigo intimo de Brahms y gran admirador de su música. La asociación era, por tanto, un ideal, y fué alcanzado un justo equilibrio por el cual el valor sinfónico de la obra se antepuso a la ejecución técnica sin que la parte de solo sufriera lo más mínimo por falta de brillantez y de efectos violinísticos. El mismo

Joachim escribió la cadencia para la primera ejecución y es todavía una de las más frecuentemente tocadas, y en justicia, aparte de su elevado mérito, debió de haber obtenido la completa aprobación del compositor. Esto hace recordar la colaboración de David, W. H. Reed y Heifetz con Mendelssohn, Elgar y Walton respectivamente para fijar la definitiva forma de las partes de solo en su concierto de violín.

La obra está concebida en gran escala y es comparable en longitud e importancia con el concierto de violín de Beethoven. El tamaño de la orquesta es, no obstante, reducido; es la orquesta clásica normal sin trombones pero con un segundo par de trompas. Aunque las trompas y las trompetas con llaves hacía ya muchos años que estaban en uso cuando esta partitura fué escrita, Brahms tenía decididas ideas acerca de la superioridad de las notas abiertas de las series armónicas y, hasta el final de su vida, usó las menos notas posibles fuera de la limitada extensión de los instrumentos 'naturales'. Esto explica el uso de un par de trompas en Re y una en Mi en los tiempos primero y último.

El primer tiempo vuelve al precedente clásico de empezar con un extenso *tutti* antes de la entrada del violín solista. En este *tutti* se halla contenida la mayor parte de los temas del tiempo. El instrumento solista aparece (compás 136) poco antes de detenerse en su exposición de los temas. Un pasaje-puente en el cual el violín tiene primero pasajes en acordes y luego marchas en semicorcheas con saltos de octava (oídas en el compás 17 del *tutti*) conduce al segundo motivo en el compás 206 y es seguido por el vigoroso pasaje (compás 246) que la orquesta había ya anunciado al final del *tutti* (compás 78). Se observará que los temas se hallan sobre el acorde tónico en el *tutti* mientras que el acorde normal dominante está empleado para el segundo motivo en la segunda por el instrumento a solo. Esto se halla de acuerdo con el procedimiento empleado por Mozart en sus Conciertos.

El desarrollo empieza en el compás 272 con otro extenso *tutti* en el que todos los temas son oídos. Una nueva acentuación rítmica aparece en el violín en el compás 312, que se extiende hasta el compás 348,

donde tiene lugar una discusión en saltos de octava. En el compás 361 empieza un pasaje que conduce a la recapitulación (compás 381) la cual se presenta en toda la orquesta ofreciendo enfáticamente el primer motivo. Los temas reaparecen en el orden anterior con algunas modificaciones. La coda comienza en el compás 527 con movimiento tranquilo, pero va poco a poco animándose hasta llegar a un final brillante. En el *animato* (compás 559) el metal y los timbales marcan el ritmo del vigoroso pasaje-puente oído en el compás 78.

El segundo tiempo está en el inesperado tono de Fa, pero el oyente es llevado al tono suavemente por los fagots, que sugieren Do menor hasta que las trompas disipan esta ilusión con su Do en el segundo compás. El oboe hace oir entonces una hermosa melodía acompañada por los instrumentos de viento. Solo es empleado un par de trompas en este tiempo y las trompetas y los timbales guardan silencio. La disposición orquestal de este pasaje confiado a los instrumentos de viento requiere para su equilibrio adecuado muy cuidadosa atención. El más ardiente defensor de Brahms no puede sostener que está bien concebido orquestalmente. El efecto es pesado y ampuloso, especialmente cuando los fagots tocan en octavas con las segundas trompas como gruñendo entre sí. Pero la melodía es idealmente adecuada para el oboe tanto por su espíritu como por el diapasón de las notas y esto compensa en gran medida la ampulosa armonización. Afortunadamente Brahms emplea la cuerda para acompañar al violín solista y los breves comentarios por los instrumentos de viento son deliciosos. La forma es simple — ternaria o de aria. La presentación de la melodía original en el compás 78 está bellamente hecha. La disposición de los instrumentos de viento a partir del compás 83 resulta mucho más agradable en sonido que lo era al principio del tiempo, y le da relieve la cuerda en el compás 87 y también (*pizzicato*) desde el compás 91. La belleza musical a traves de todo este pasaje no está perturbada por ninguna indiscreción de la partitura. Esperamos siempre cierta densidad en la manera de Brahms; es parte de su estilo y se acomoda a la seriedad de su temperamento. Sólo ocasionalmente llega a ser molesto.

Joachim era húngaro y debido principalmente a su influencia Brahms llegó a interesarse por la música húngara y gitana, como puede verse reflejado al final de este concierto. El tiempo es alegre y amplio y aparece como un grande y deseado contraste con la gravedad de los tiempos anteriores. Tiene la forma de rondó libre. Usamos la palabra 'libre' porque se hallan bastante desarrollados los motivos. Los principales son (a) el oído al comienzo con su correspondencia en el compás 17 y repetición en el 27; (b) el ascendente en octavas en el violín solista y en el compás 57, y (c) el tema a tres tiempos en el compás 128.

Brahms tiene cuidado en evitar demasiada cuadratura de ritmo en su principal motivo, como se observa en los compases 31–33. La escritura para el violín solista muestra gran brillantez a traves de todo el tiempo y solo pudo haber sido trazada por un violinista. Joachim parece haber tenido aquí entera libertad en la escritura de la parte del violín, no sólo en la manera de corregir pasajes para la mejor conveniencia de la mano izquierda, sino también en la importantísima cuestión de la técnica del arco, los detalles de la cual pueden a menudo ser sólo conseguidos probando en el instrumento.

La coda empieza en el compás 222 y se divide en dos partes, empezando la segunda en el *Poco fini presto* que sigue la breve cadencia en el compás 266. En la segunda parte de la coda el tema principal está presentado en el compás de 6/8 (escrito como tresillos) y hay tambien nuevo tratamiento del tema (b) y su inversión (empezando en el compás 292). El final es tan original como efectivo. En vez de terminar con valentía Brahms deja a la música apagarse en la distancia, y el acorde final *forte*, no *fortíssimo*, está añadido como parada decisiva.

El concierto es una de las más conseguidas obras de Brahms. Los temas y su tratamiento se señalan a través de él por los más grandes aciertos de invención. Se ha sostenido durante setenta y cinco años en un alto y honroso sitio en el limitado repertorio de primera categoria de los contos de violín y continuará en él en el porvenir. Es un espléndido ejemplo del virtuosismo sirviendo puramente a los fines musicales.

Pueden añadirse algunas palabras acerca de los instrumentos transpositores. Los clarinetes en La se emplean en los tiempos primero y último. Suenan una tercera menor más baja de lo que aparecen escritos. En el tiempo lento se emplean clarinetes en Si bemol. Estos suenan un tono más bajo que la escritura. Las trompas en Re transponen una séptima menor y las en Mi una sexta menor baja excepto cuando sus partes están escritas en la clave baja. Entonces suben un tono entero y una tercera mayor respectivamente. En el tiempo lento se emplean trompas en Fa. Estas transponen una quinta inferior si están escritas en la clave alta y una cuarta superior si en la clave baja. Las trompetas en Re transponen un tono alto.

Violin Concerto in D major

I

22

P. 25

26

28

34

39

40

44

47

poco rit.

52

340

56

58

P. 25

P. 25

61

64

470

>*p lusingando*

P. 25

69

II

8o

P. 25

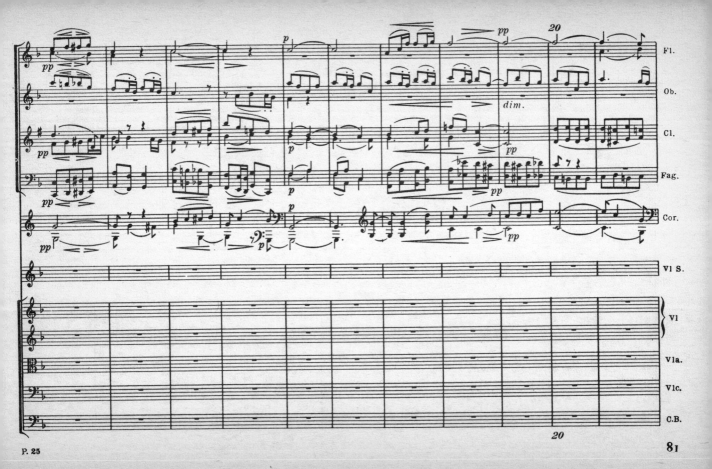

86 P. 25

90

P. 25

P. 25

93

III

Allegro giocoso, ma non troppo vivace

Fl.
Ob.
Cl.
Fag.

1 2
Cor.
3 4
Tr.
Timp.

Vl.S.

Vl.
Vla.
Vlc.
C.B.

112

116

P. 25

118

Fl.

Ob.

Cl.

Fag.

1 2
Cor.
3 4

Tr.

Timp.

Vl.S.

Vl.

Vla.

Vlc.

C.B.

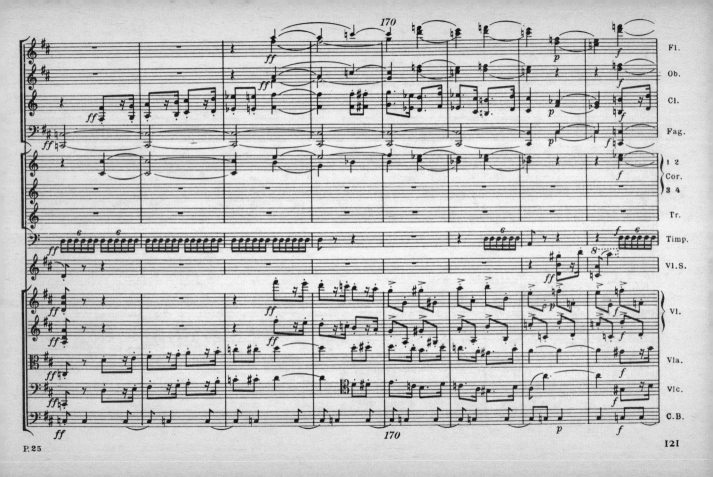

134.

Fl.
Ob.
Cl.
Fag.
1 2
Cor.
3 4
Tr.
Timp.
Vl.S.
Vl.
Vla.
Vlc.
C.B.

143